Mysteries of Nature

by Anne Miranda
illustrated by Rick Brown

Harcourt

Orlando   Boston   Dallas   Chicago   San Diego

Visit *The Learning Site!*

www.harcourtschool.com

"Good morning, boys and girls. Miss Tourees is my name, and mysteries are my game. I am a detective. I snoop around to find the facts of a case. I check to see whether everyone is telling the truth. I make sure each person has an alibi. In short, I get to the bottom of things. That's all you need to know about what I do. Let's get straightaway to your questions!"

"I've got a question," muttered a boy in the back.

"Pardon?" asked Miss Tourees.

"Isn't that what a condemned person gets from the governor?" retorted the boy.

"Very funny," chirped Miss Tourees. "Did you have a question?"

"Yes, you can solve a mystery for me. What is a rainbow?" asked the boy.

"That's not my kind of mystery. However, I do happen to know the answer," said Miss Tourees. She opened her purse and took out a triangular piece of glass. "This is a prism. When I hold the prism to the light, what happens?"

"Look at all the colors!" said a girl with freckles.

"The prism slows the light and bends it. This separates the white light into its different parts. White light is actually a combination of violet, indigo, blue, green, yellow, orange, and red light—all the colors in a rainbow."

"How do the colors get up to the sky?" asked a boy with a missing tooth.

"When it rains, the raindrops act like a huge prism. When the light shines through the rain just so, we see a rainbow in the sky," answered Miss Tourees.

A girl in a purple shirt raised her hand. "Northern lights are pretty, like a rainbow. What makes them?"

"The northern lights are indeed colorful. However, the aurora borealis is not caused by tiny drops of water," said Miss Tourees. She took a magnet out of her purse and used it to pick up a bunch of paper clips from Miss Fitz's desk. "Earth is like a big magnet. It has two magnetic poles. One is at the top of Earth and one is at the bottom. The magnetic force at the North Pole pulls solar particles flying through space toward Earth, just like this magnet pulls on the paper clips. When these solar particles hit gases in our atmosphere, they light the sky like fireworks on the Fourth of July."

"Speaking of the Fourth of July," began another student, "I was at the beach last year. Suddenly, the water was sucked up from the sea. It spun around and around in the air, like clay spinning on a sculptor's wheel. It was beautiful and scary at the same time. It was the most mysterious thing I've ever seen."

Miss Tourees smiled. "What you saw was a waterspout. It's a tornado, only over the water. A chain of unusual conditions causes a waterspout. A column of hot air rises suddenly from the land or the ocean. To understand how this works, imagine a pot of water heating on a stove. When it gets to a certain temperature, strings of bubbles rise in columns from the bottom of the pot. The air in the atmosphere can act the same way when it's hot."

"Is that all there is to it?" asked the student.

"No, there's more. Strong winds also play a role in strengthening a waterspout. The wind spins around the column of rising air. Extreme low pressure inside the column pulls the spinning wind up with tremendous force. When this powerful whirlwind touches the ocean, it sucks up water like soda through a straw. That's a waterspout," said Miss Tourees.

"How is a dust devil formed?" asked another pupil.

"A dust devil is formed the same way, but on a much smaller scale. It is a miniature tornado that picks up dust, especially on hot, dry, windy days."

"Once I saw someone stick a straw through a potato. How can anyone do that? It's still a mystery to me," said a baffled boy with black hair.

"Hmmm. That does seem like a mystery, doesn't it? But sticking a straw through a potato or an apple like the one on Miss Fitz's desk is pure science," said Miss Tourees. She took a straw from her purse, picked up the apple, and drove the straw through it like a nail.

The class applauded wildly.

"Inside this straw is a column of air. When I put my thumb over the end of the straw, it creates pressure inside the straw. When the straw hits the apple, the air inside the straw pushes through the apple. Isn't that amazing?"

The class said, "Oooooo."

7

A girl with brown hair raised her hand. "Miss Tourees, I am reading a detective story. . ."

"At last someone wants to know about the cases I've solved!" interrupted Miss Tourees.

"No, actually, I wanted to know what a natural bridge is. There's one mentioned in my book," said the girl.

"Bridges are built by people. A natural bridge is made by nature. It is a stone arch that is made by a combination of wind, rain, heat, and cold. These forces act like a chisel to make a hole in the rock. Weathering sandstone forms many natural bridges. Natural bridges often occur in deserts. Any other questions? How about a question about the Case of the Missing Case?"

Man-Made

Natural

An enthusiastic boy in a blue shirt asked, "Have you ever solved a case involving Mexican jumping beans? I have a bunch here in my pocket. What makes them jump?"

"No, I have never solved a case involving Mexican jumping beans," said Miss Tourees as she took the jumping beans from the boy. "What do you think makes them jump?" she asked, showing them to the class.

"Magnets!" said one student.

"Bubbles of hot air," suggested another.

"Magic," said a third.

"Good guesses," smiled Miss Tourees, "but the correct answer is insects. There is a tiny beetle grub inside each one. As the grub turns, the bean jumps. Pretty cool, yes?"

"I have a question," said a girl with red hair. "Are there really dragons?"

"We read about many creatures such as dragons, griffins, giant squids, and mermaids in books. Human beings like to invent imaginative stories. Sometimes these stories help us with our fears. Making up a story about something we are afraid of helps us feel less scared. Of these four, only the giant squid actually exists. The others are mythical. They don't exist in real life."

"Really?" gasped the girl.

"Really," said Miss Tourees. "There is no proof that dragons existed. No dragon fossils have ever been found. Since dragons exist only in our imagination, we won't find any bones."

"Could dinosaurs and dragons be the same?" asked the girl.

"Dinosaurs died out millions of years before humans appeared on Earth. We have found many dinosaur skeletons. Dragons supposedly lived at the same time people did. However, there are no dragon skeletons. So dinosaurs and dragons cannot be the same."

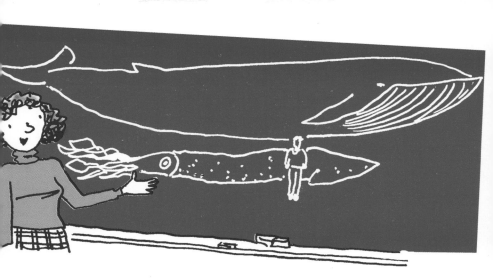

"Who says there are giant squids?" asked a tall boy.

"People have found them washed up on beaches. The record size is 59 feet long. Giant squids have huge eyes. Each one is the size of a watermelon!"

"Why aren't there any giant squids in the City Aquarium?" asked the tall boy.

"No one has seen one alive. Giant squids live deep in the ocean. People cannot travel to those depths."

"Is it possible that dragons live where people can't see them?" asked the boy. "Maybe dragons are just well hidden. Just because we can't see something doesn't mean it doesn't exist."

"It might be possible," said Miss Tourees. "That's why people still try to solve those mysteries."

A girl in orange sneakers raised her hand. "I heard that if a sea star or starfish loses an arm, it can grow another one. Is that true?"

"Yes, that is true," said Miss Tourees. "Several kinds of animals can grow new body parts. Sea stars can grow new arms. There is a kind of lizard that can break off part of its tail when it is caught. It grows another tail in its place. Some plants can make new plants from stems or leaves that are cut from the mother plant. Only a few animals can grow new parts. How they do this is being studied."

"Why?" asked the girl in the orange sneakers.

"Suppose doctors could help other animals or people grow new arms or legs," said Miss Tourees. "That would be wonderful!"

"What is a clone?" asked a boy in a plaid shirt.

"A clone is an exact copy of an animal," said Miss Tourees. "Cloning is hard. It has been done, though. The inside of one animal's cell is put inside the egg of a host animal. This altered egg is implanted in the host. The baby grows inside the host animal and is born. The cells of the baby animal are the same as those of the first animal. The most famous clone is Dolly, the sheep. Dolly grew up normally and had a normal baby. So cloning works."

"Why would anyone want to clone a sheep? Aren't there about a trillion sheep in the world?" asked the boy.

"Scientists think that if they can clone sheep, they can clone other animals. For example, they could clone endangered animals. Farm animals could give birth to rare animals. In this way whole species could be saved."

"Could dinosaurs be cloned?" asked a girl in the third row.

"No, I don't think so. Scientists would have to find dinosaur cells. Dinosaur fossils do not have cells. The dinosaur bones we see in museums are stone. Under pressure and over time, minerals fill and replace the bones," said Miss Tourees. "I think cloning a dinosaur would be impossible."

"Scientists have found frozen woolly mammoths. Could they clone those?" asked the girl.

"Hmmm. Frozen cells of the woolly mammoths might be intact. Finding a host would be a problem. Maybe scientists could use an elephant. It might work. However, nothing as big as an elephant has ever been cloned."

"Would cloning an extinct animal be a good idea?" the girl asked.

14

"It's difficult to answer that question. I just don't know," said Miss Tourees.

"I thought you knew everything," said a boy in jeans.

Miss Tourees laughed. "My dear children, no one can know everything. It's impossible to know everything. What a dull and boring world we would live in if we could know everything. There would be no reason to get up in the morning. There would be no reason to investigate mysteries. Why, I'd be out of a job! Then I would have no reason to come to your class for Career Day."

"What kinds of things do you investigate?" asked the boy. "I'm curious to know what cases you've solved."

"I'm glad you asked," said Miss Tourees. "I've been waiting all morning for someone to ask that question."

Suddenly, the bell rang.

"Our class is over," said Miss Fitz, coming to the front of the room.

"Oh, no! I haven't told them about the Case of the Slippery Snake or the Case of the Haunted Mansion!" said Miss Tourees.

"Maybe next time. Class, please thank Miss Tourees for her excellent talk on nature's mysteries," said Miss Fitz.

"Thank you, Miss Tourees," chimed the class.

"Remember your homework assignment," said Miss Fitz as the children filed out of the room. "Explain how to solve one of nature's mysteries!"